INTERNET THEME SERIES

Endangered Species

Anne Salerno

World Teachers Press

Order Number 2-5071
ISBN 1-885111-87-8

A B C D E F 99 00 01 02

Educational Resources

395 Main Street
Rowley, MA 01969

Foreword

The Internet is an awesome and remarkable two-way communication device and can bring a wealth of information right to the classroom.

This **Internet Theme Series** promotes constructive use of the Internet and is designed to help students develop:

- an awareness of the Internet;
- skills as an Internet user;
- knowledge of specific theme areas; and
- important language and research skills.

Students simply go to the Didax Web site as directed at the top of each worksheet. From there they will be easily guided to the relevant Web site where they can begin their worksheets. Clear and precise instructions guide the students carefully through the high-interest activities.

Each book in the series is based on a popular theme and provides carefully-designed worksheets directing students to use information gathered from the Internet. The worksheets are language-based and aim to develop comprehension, writing, word study and research skills through theme topics.

A detailed, step-by-step guide to the use of this book along with answers provided at the back of the book make it a very teacher-friendly package.

This book looks at **Endangered Species**. Students are made aware of specific vulnerable and endangered animals and their present situation. Some of the tasks include designing a zoo enclosure, writing a procedure for and making an eagle kite and recording facts about the elephant's ears and trunk.

Students will have a lot of fun exploring the Web sites and gaining valuable skills and information.

Contents

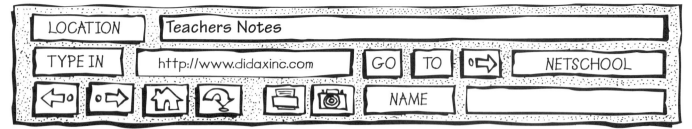

In this book students will be directed to relevant Internet sites through a process of linking.

- The starting point is the Didax home page located at:

http://www.didaxinc.com

IT IS RECOMMENDED THAT YOU BOOKMARK THIS SITE FOR QUICKER AND EASIER ACCESS.

- Click on the link to Netschool

- Click on the appropriate link

- Find link for corresponding activity page

By its nature the Internet is like the ocean, fluid and forever-changing. For many reasons a site may change, relocate to another address or simply disappear. Please note that some site/servers can be down for short periods of time and it may need to be revisited at another time.

Should you have problems locating a site in this series, please e-mail us from our home page. Regular checks and updates by the publisher should ensure easy access to the world of the Internet.

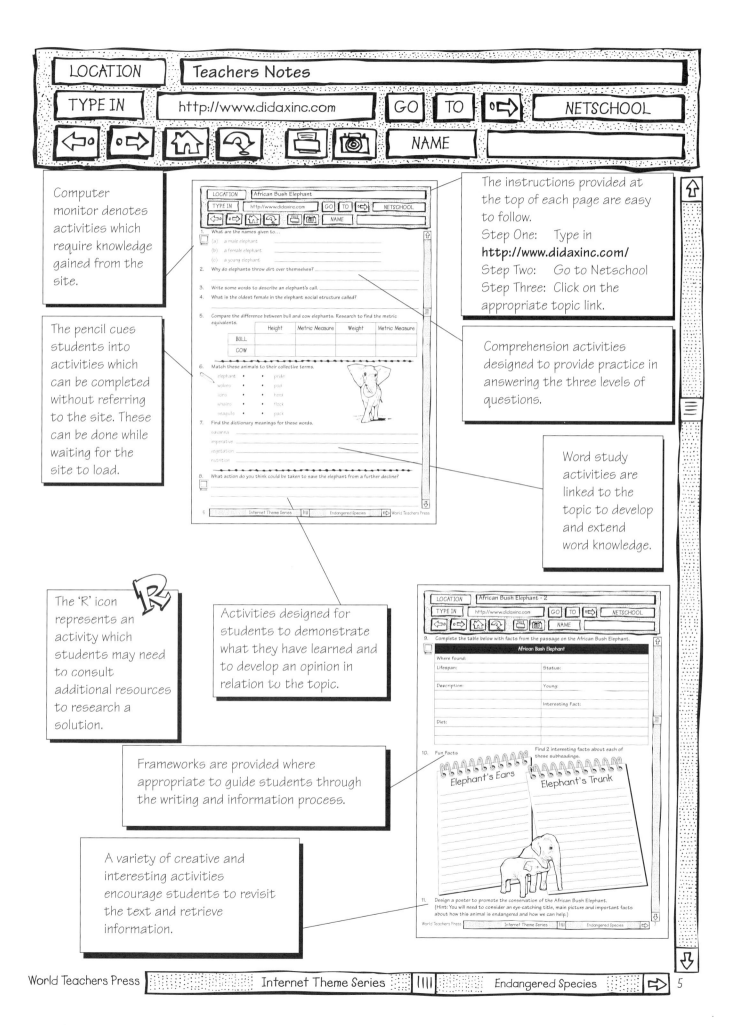

Computer monitor denotes activities which require knowledge gained from the site.

The pencil cues students into activities which can be completed without referring to the site. These can be done while waiting for the site to load.

The 'R' icon represents an activity which students may need to consult additional resources to research a solution.

The instructions provided at the top of each page are easy to follow.
Step One: Type in
http://www.didaxinc.com/
Step Two: Go to Netschool
Step Three: Click on the appropriate topic link.

Comprehension activities designed to provide practice in answering the three levels of questions.

Word study activities are linked to the topic to develop and extend word knowledge.

Activities designed for students to demonstrate what they have learned and to develop an opinion in relation to the topic.

Frameworks are provided where appropriate to guide students through the writing and information process.

A variety of creative and interesting activities encourage students to revisit the text and retrieve information.

NAME

1. **What are the names given to...**

   (a) a male elephant _____

   (b) a female elephant _____

   (c) a young elephant _____

2. **Why do elephants throw dirt over themselves?** _____
   _____

3. **Write some words to describe an elephant's call.** _____

4. **What is the oldest female in the elephant social structure called?**
   _____

5. **Compare the difference between bull and cow elephants. Research to find the metric equivalents.**

	Height	Metric Measure	Weight	Metric Measure
BULL				
COW				

6. **Match these animals to their collective terms.**

   elephant •   • pride

   wolves •   • pod

   lions •   • herd

   whales •   • flock

   seagulls •   • pack

7. **Find the dictionary meanings for these words.**

   savanna _____

   imperative _____

   vegetation _____

   nutrition _____

8. **What action do you think could be taken to save the elephant from a further decline?**
   _____
   _____

TYPE IN · http://www.didaxinc.com · GO TO · NETSCHOOL · NAME

9. Complete the table below with facts from the passage on the African Bush Elephant.

African Bush Elephant	
Where found:	
Lifespan:	Status:
Description:	Young:
	Interesting Fact:
Diet:	

10. Fun Facts

Find 2 interesting facts about each of these subheadings.

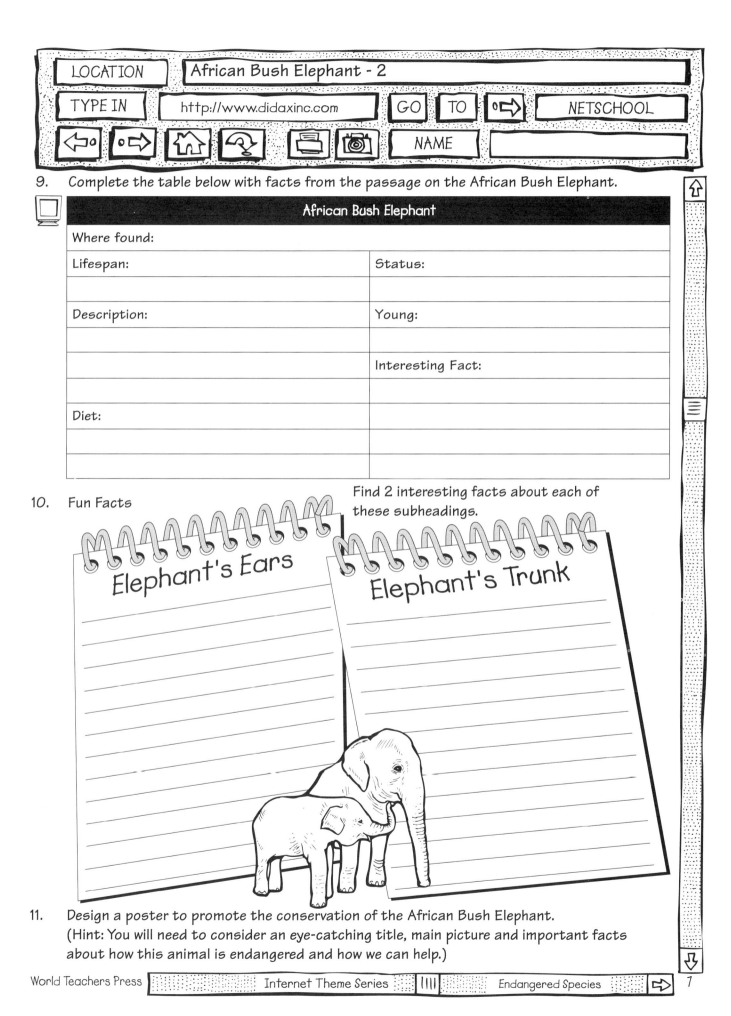

Elephant's Ears

Elephant's Trunk

11. Design a poster to promote the conservation of the African Bush Elephant.
(Hint: You will need to consider an eye-catching title, main picture and important facts about how this animal is endangered and how we can help.)

1. Rewrite these words in alphabetical order.

Word	Alphabetical Order
wing	
white	
wingspan	
water	
weigh	
winter	

2. Underline the nouns in blue and circle the verbs in red in these sentences.

(a) Bald eagles nest on the edge of rivers, lakes or seashores.

(b) Bald eagles commonly feed on fish which they catch themselves.

(c) They also feed on a variety of live prey including waterfowl, birds, turtles and rabbits.

3. Color and label this drawing of the bald eagle.

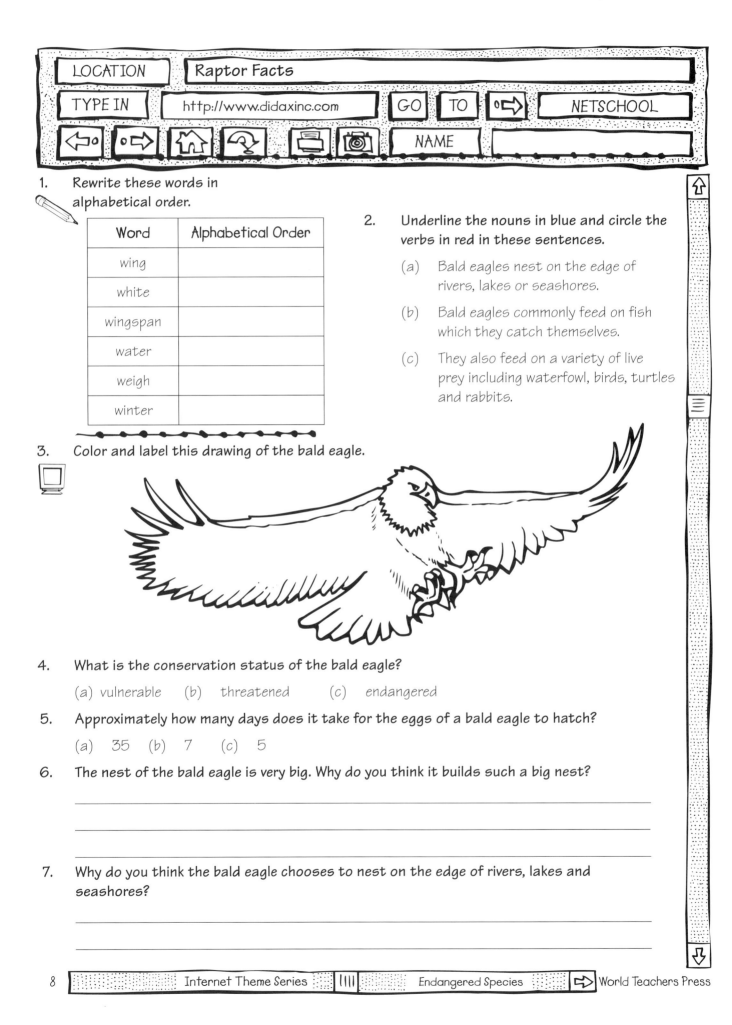

4. What is the conservation status of the bald eagle?

(a) vulnerable   (b) threatened   (c) endangered

5. Approximately how many days does it take for the eggs of a bald eagle to hatch?

(a) 35   (b) 7   (c) 5

6. The nest of the bald eagle is very big. Why do you think it builds such a big nest?

_____

_____

_____

7. Why do you think the bald eagle chooses to nest on the edge of rivers, lakes and seashores?

_____

_____

8. Here is your chance to make a bald eagle kite. We have provided you with the pictures, now write the procedure and make your kite.

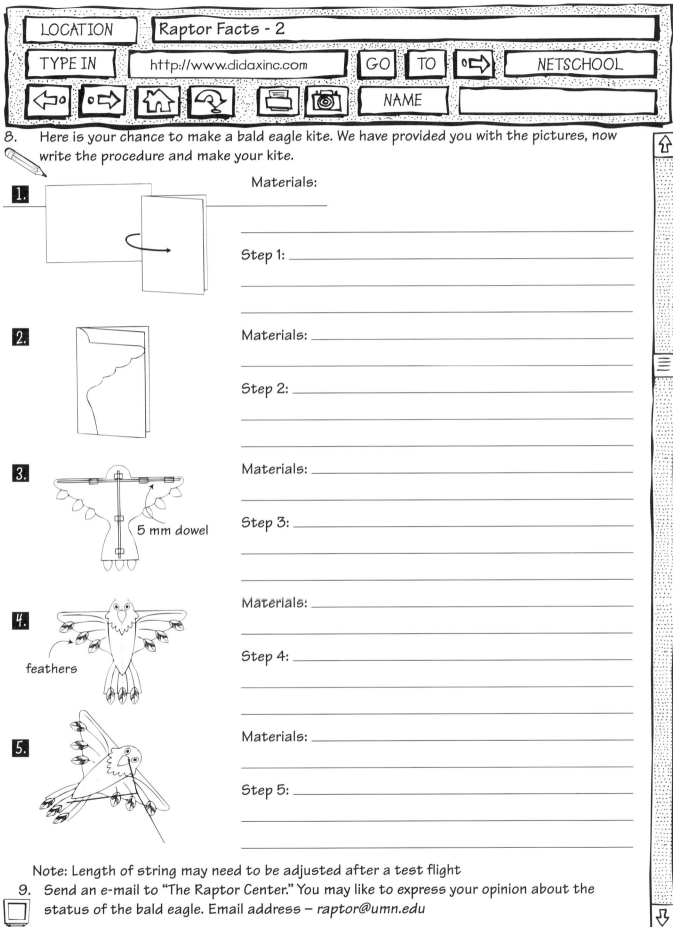

1.

Materials:

_____

Step 1: _____

_____

_____

2.

Materials: _____

Step 2: _____

_____

_____

3.

5 mm dowel

Materials: _____

Step 3: _____

_____

_____

4.

feathers

Materials: _____

Step 4: _____

_____

_____

5.

Materials: _____

Step 5: _____

_____

_____

Note: Length of string may need to be adjusted after a test flight

9. Send an e-mail to "The Raptor Center." You may like to express your opinion about the status of the bald eagle. Email address – raptor@umn.edu

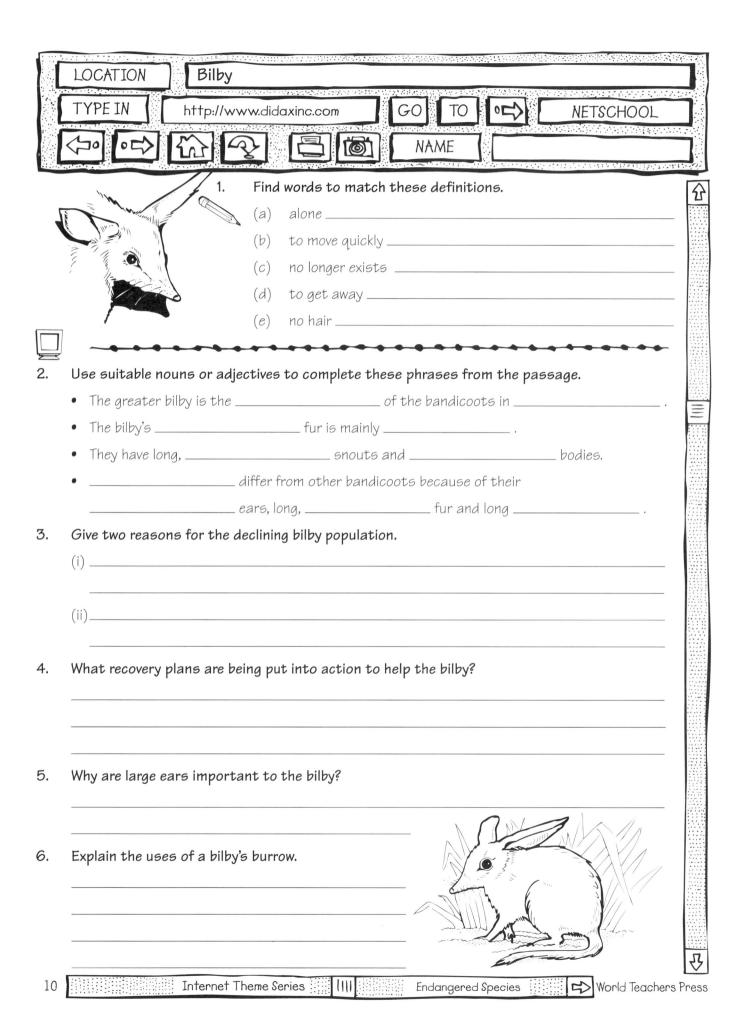

LOCATION	Bilby
TYPE IN	http://www.didaxinc.com	GO	TO	▢⇨	NETSCHOOL

NAME

1. Find words to match these definitions.

(a) alone _____

(b) to move quickly _____

(c) no longer exists _____

(d) to get away _____

(e) no hair _____

2. Use suitable nouns or adjectives to complete these phrases from the passage.

- The greater bilby is the _____ of the bandicoots in _____ .

- The bilby's _____ fur is mainly _____ .

- They have long, _____ snouts and _____ bodies.

- _____ differ from other bandicoots because of their

  _____ ears, long, _____ fur and long _____ .

3. Give two reasons for the declining bilby population.

(i) _____

_____

(ii) _____

_____

4. What recovery plans are being put into action to help the bilby?

_____

_____

_____

5. Why are large ears important to the bilby?

_____

_____

6. Explain the uses of a bilby's burrow.

_____

_____

_____

_____

LOCATION | Bilby - 2

TYPE IN | http://www.didaxinc.com | GO | TO | NETSCHOOL

NAME

7. Select three paragraphs from the passage 'Bilby'. Write key words or phrases for each paragraph to show the main idea.

Paragraph 1	Key Words/Phrases
Key Sentence	

Paragraph 2	Key Words/Phrases
Key Sentence	

Paragraph 3	Key Words/Phrases	Key Sentence

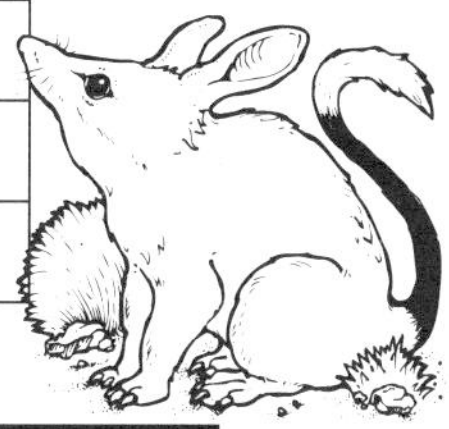

8. Find facts from the passage to complete the table below.

Description	Habitat	Young	Diet/Food

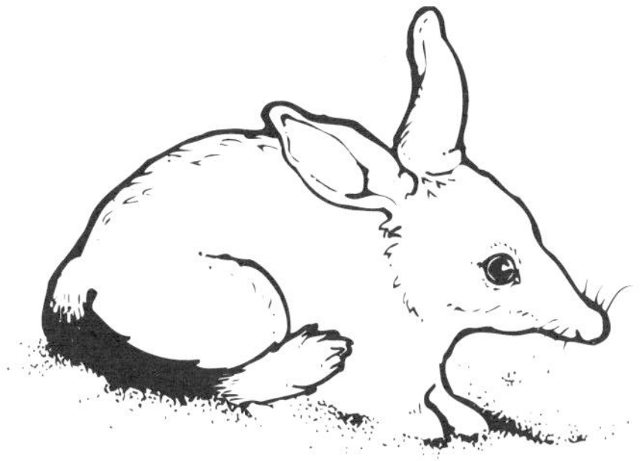

9. What are the Aboriginal terms for the bilby?

10. How can we help in the conservation of this animal?

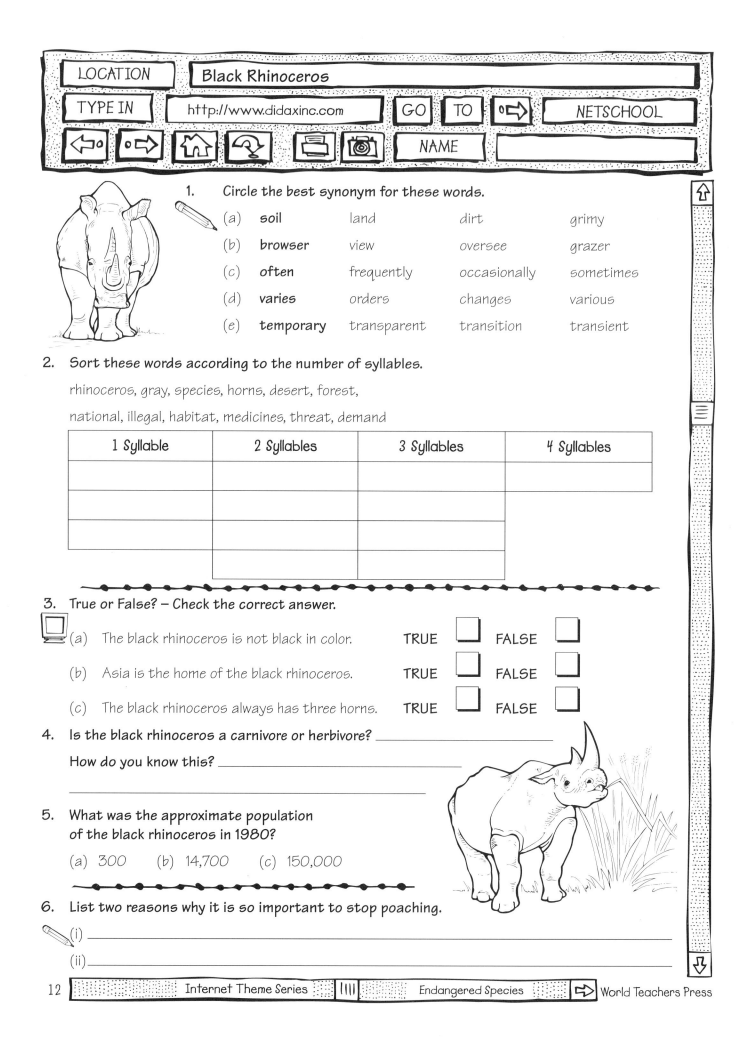

1. Circle the best synonym for these words.

   (a) **soil**   land   dirt   grimy

   (b) **browser**   view   oversee   grazer

   (c) **often**   frequently   occasionally   sometimes

   (d) **varies**   orders   changes   various

   (e) **temporary**   transparent   transition   transient

2. Sort these words according to the number of syllables.

   rhinoceros, gray, species, horns, desert, forest,

   national, illegal, habitat, medicines, threat, demand

1 Syllable	2 Syllables	3 Syllables	4 Syllables

3. True or False? – Check the correct answer.

   (a) The black rhinoceros is not black in color.   TRUE ☐   FALSE ☐

   (b) Asia is the home of the black rhinoceros.   TRUE ☐   FALSE ☐

   (c) The black rhinoceros always has three horns.   TRUE ☐   FALSE ☐

4. Is the black rhinoceros a carnivore or herbivore? _____

   How do you know this? _____

   _____

5. What was the approximate population
   of the black rhinoceros in 1980?

   (a) 300   (b) 14,700   (c) 150,000

6. List two reasons why it is so important to stop poaching.

   (i) _____

   (ii) _____

7. Design a wildlife park environment that will protect the black rhinoceros from poaching and allow numbers to increase. You will need to complete the following and provide support for your ideas.

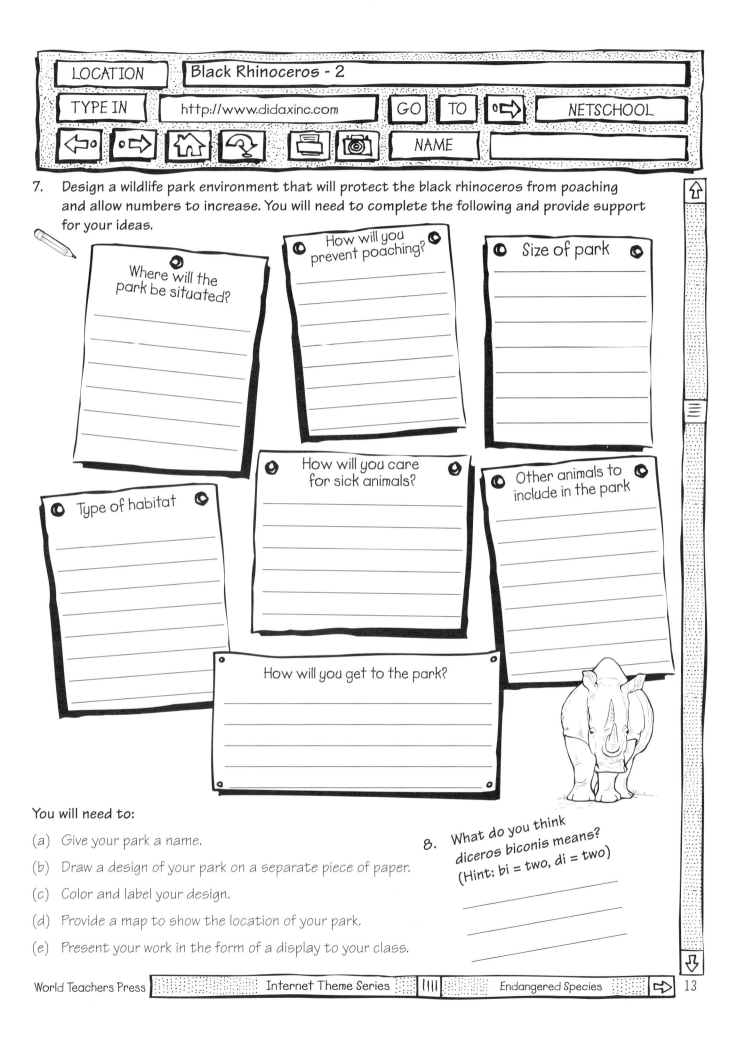

Where will the park be situated?

How will you prevent poaching?

Size of park

Type of habitat

How will you care for sick animals?

Other animals to include in the park

How will you get to the park?

You will need to:

(a) Give your park a name.

(b) Draw a design of your park on a separate piece of paper.

(c) Color and label your design.

(d) Provide a map to show the location of your park.

(e) Present your work in the form of a display to your class.

8. What do you think *diceros biconis* means?
(Hint: bi = two, di = two)

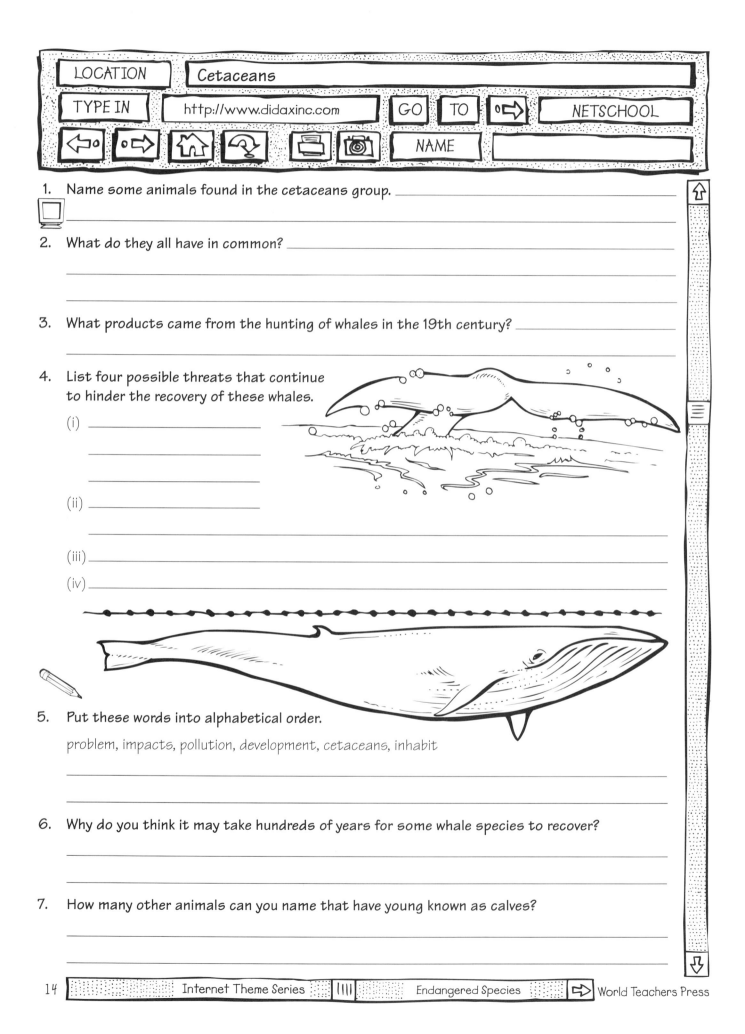

1. Name some animals found in the cetaceans group. _____
_____

2. What do they all have in common? _____
_____
_____

3. What products came from the hunting of whales in the 19th century? _____
_____

4. List four possible threats that continue to hinder the recovery of these whales.

(i) _____
_____

(ii) _____
_____

(iii) _____

(iv) _____

5. Put these words into alphabetical order.

problem, impacts, pollution, development, cetaceans, inhabit

_____
_____

6. Why do you think it may take hundreds of years for some whale species to recover?
_____
_____

7. How many other animals can you name that have young known as calves?
_____
_____

LOCATION | Cetaceans - 2

TYPE IN | http://www.didaxinc.com | GO | TO | NETSCHOOL

NAME

8. Use the information from the Cetaceans passage to complete the chart below. Choose two whale species of your own.

Species	Description	Diet	Special Features/Facts
Blue Whale			
Humpback Whale			

9. Debate the issues of hunting whales as opposed to conserving whales. Write main points both for and against these issues. Set up debating teams to discuss your ideas.

1. Alliteration occurs when words beginning with the same letters are used to form a phrase about a topic (e.g., Susan slowly stretches).

Use alliteration to form animal phrases in the box below.

Adjective (Describing)	Noun (Naming)	Verb (Doing)	Adverb (How?)
sleepy	snakes		
	cheetah		carefully
	gorilla		
	dog	digs	
	fish		

2. List three causes leading to the cheetah being classed as endangered.

   (i) _____

   (ii) _____

   (iii) _____

3. How does the cheetah catch its prey? _____

   _____

   _____

4. Why does it hunt in the day more than any other cat? _____

   _____

5. Describe and draw the cheetah's coat.

   _____

   _____

   _____

6. How do you think its coloring helps the cheetah? _____

   _____

LOCATION: Cheetah - 2

TYPE IN: http://www.didaxinc.com GO TO NETSCHOOL

NAME

7. Use facts or key phrases from the passage to complete the table below.

CHEETAH	Grouping (solitary, pairs...)	Description	Interesting Facts
Male			
Female			
Cubs			

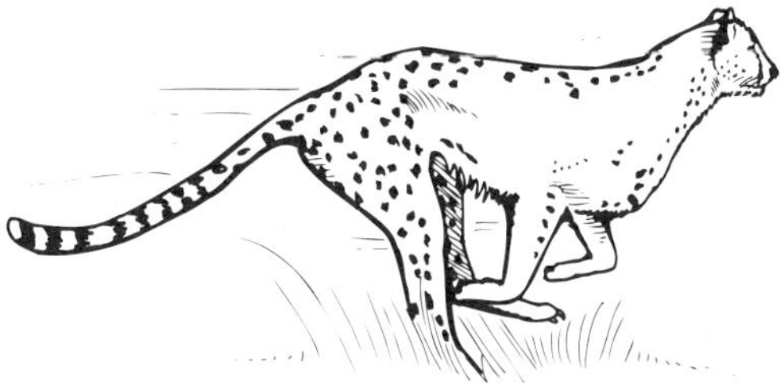

8. What attributes do you think the cheetah has to enable it to move so fast?

9. Given the problem, explain the effect you think it would have on the cheetah population.

Cause	Effect
The continual destruction of habitat to enlarge farming areas.	
The ability to breed cheetahs successfully in captivity.	
The re-introduction of commercial trading of furs.	
A huge increase in the impala and gazelle populations.	

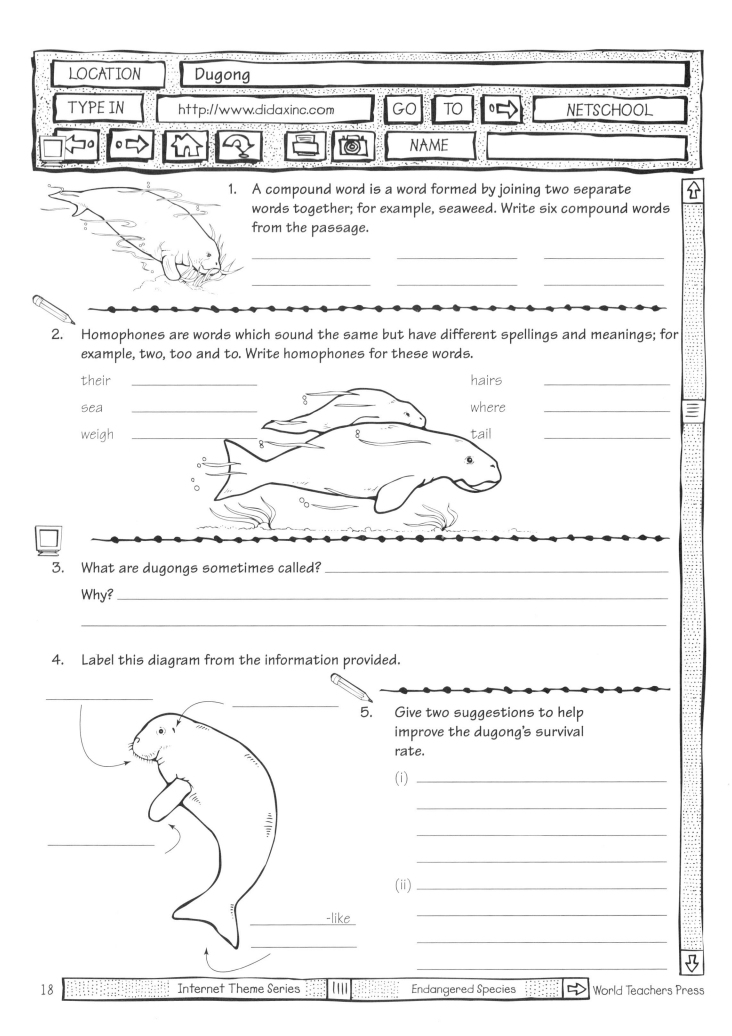

1. A compound word is a word formed by joining two separate words together; for example, seaweed. Write six compound words from the passage.

_____ _____ _____

_____ _____ _____

2. Homophones are words which sound the same but have different spellings and meanings; for example, two, too and to. Write homophones for these words.

their _____ hairs _____

sea _____ where _____

weigh _____ tail _____

3. What are dugongs sometimes called? _____

Why? _____

_____

4. Label this diagram from the information provided.

_____

_____

_____

_____-like

_____

5. Give two suggestions to help improve the dugong's survival rate.

(i) _____

_____

_____

_____

(ii) _____

_____

_____

_____

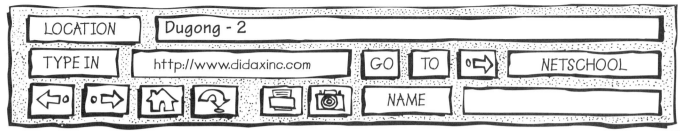
6. Label this map of Australia and shade the areas where dugongs are found.

7. You have been employed by the Museum of Sea Sciences to create a display on dugongs. The display must:

  • educate the public about the plight of the dugong;

  • contain a model of a dugong and her calf;

  • show the ideal habitat for a dugong; and

  • provide information to the public about what they can do to ensure the dugong survives and their population increases.

Use this brief to create a display for your classroom. Remember, it must be easy to assemble and include all aspects listed above.

8. Find more about the effects of farming on Australian waterways. What is being done to protect the waterways?

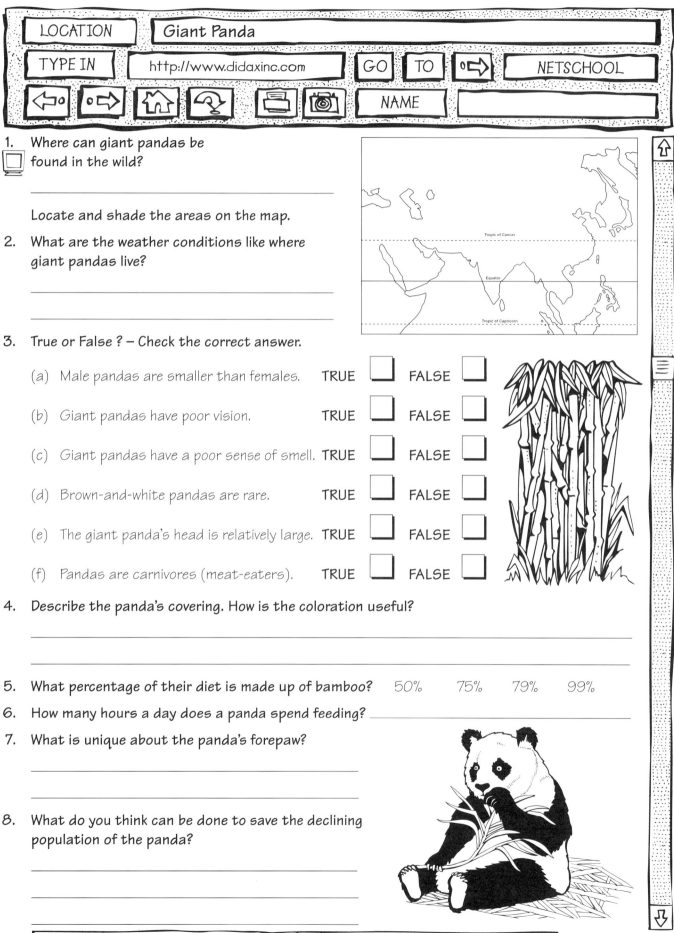

LOCATION | Giant Panda

TYPE IN | http://www.didaxinc.com | GO | TO | ▢⇨ | NETSCHOOL

NAME

1. Where can giant pandas be found in the wild?

_____

Locate and shade the areas on the map.

2. What are the weather conditions like where giant pandas live?

_____

_____

Tropic of Cancer

Equator

Tropic of Capricorn

3. True or False ? – Check the correct answer.

(a) Male pandas are smaller than females.　TRUE ▢　FALSE ▢

(b) Giant pandas have poor vision.　TRUE ▢　FALSE ▢

(c) Giant pandas have a poor sense of smell.　TRUE ▢　FALSE ▢

(d) Brown-and-white pandas are rare.　TRUE ▢　FALSE ▢

(e) The giant panda's head is relatively large.　TRUE ▢　FALSE ▢

(f) Pandas are carnivores (meat-eaters).　TRUE ▢　FALSE ▢

4. Describe the panda's covering. How is the coloration useful?

_____

_____

5. What percentage of their diet is made up of bamboo?　50%　75%　79%　99%

6. How many hours a day does a panda spend feeding? _____

7. What is unique about the panda's forepaw?

_____

_____

8. What do you think can be done to save the declining population of the panda?

_____

_____

_____

9. Use the timeline below to record important steps taken to conserve the giant panda.

1957

1993

1986

1996

10. List three conservation management plans from the 1989 proposals.

(i) _____

(ii) _____

(iii) _____

Loss of bamboo forests further threat to pandas

Captivity program success: hope for the giant panda

Own Choice:

11. Choose one of these news headlines or develop one of your own about the giant panda. Plan your article in the information box below. Use information from this site to help you take notes.

When?	Who?	Where?	What?	Why?	Conclusion

Use this plan to write a full newspaper article. Join with other classmates to make an informative newspaper about giant pandas. Make a classroom display.

1. **Find the meaning of these terms.**

   (a) mountainous _____

   (b) abandoned _____

   (c) lowland _____

   (d) cultivated _____

   (e) altitude _____

2. **Write suitable antonyms for the words in bold print in these sentences.**

   (a) Gorillas **never** strip a feed site bare. _____

   (b) Silverbacks are very **large**. _____

   (c) Gorillas **seldom** drink water. _____

   (d) Female gorillas tend to be **shorter**. _____

   (e) Gorillas are **found** in Africa. _____

3. **True or False? – Check the correct answer.**

   (a) Gorillas always walk on two feet. TRUE ☐ FALSE ☐

   (b) Gorillas have small, dark brown eyes. TRUE ☐ FALSE ☐

   (c) Birds and small animals are part of the gorilla's diet. TRUE ☐ FALSE ☐

   (d) Grasping objects is very easy for a gorilla. TRUE ☐ FALSE ☐

4. **What does the phrase 'primarily terrestrial' mean?**

   _____

   _____

5. **What is the meaning of 'locomotion'?**

   _____

   _____

6. **Give your opinion about gorillas learning sign language and being taught to form simple sentences.** _____

   _____

   _____

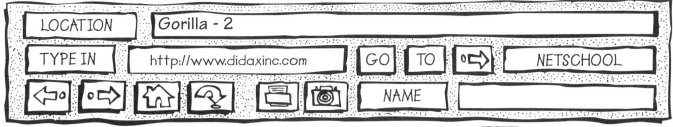

7. Newspapers and media often report on the diminishing numbers of the gorilla. A newspaper headline may be...

Can you write two more catchy headlines?

Where have the gorillas gone?

8. You are the publishing manager of a successful magazine and have recently returned from your annual leave, which you spent in Africa. While there, you became aware of the rapid decline in the numbers of the mountain gorilla. You have decided to devote a double page spread providing information and pictures to educate your readers about the plight of the mountain gorilla. You will need to include the following.

Where found _____

Estimated population _____

Preferred habitat _____

Diet _____

Problems faced _____

_____

_____

_____

How people can help _____

_____

_____

_____

Put together your double page spread and present the finished product to the class.

1. If a male polar bear is a boar and a female is a sow, what are these?

Animal	Male	Female
	stallion	
		ewe
swan		
rabbit		
		hen
	stag	

2. The large paws of a polar bear act like snowshoes, spreading the bear's weight over the ice. Circle the words that can be added to 'snow' to make compound words.

grass   drift   field   flake   dog

Write the new word and its

definition on a separate

berry   **SNOW**   ball   cat   drop   piece of paper.

daisy

woman   man   pea

3. Complete this table.

Height	Male		Female	
Weight	Male		Female	
Color	Fur		Skin	
Eyes				
Ears				
Tail				
Coat				

4. What is the status of the polar bear?

(a) vulnerable   (b) threatened   (c) endangered

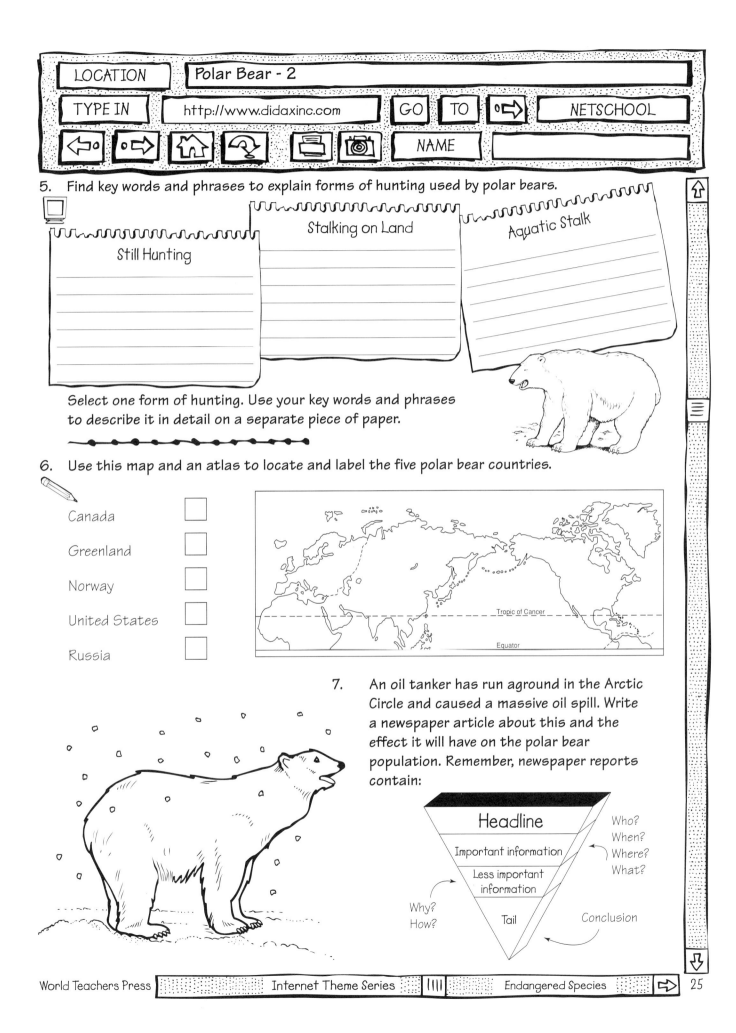

5. Find key words and phrases to explain forms of hunting used by polar bears.

Still Hunting

Stalking on Land

Aquatic Stalk

Select one form of hunting. Use your key words and phrases to describe it in detail on a separate piece of paper.

6. Use this map and an atlas to locate and label the five polar bear countries.

Canada ☐

Greenland ☐

Norway ☐

United States ☐

Russia ☐

Tropic of Cancer

Equator

7. An oil tanker has run aground in the Arctic Circle and caused a massive oil spill. Write a newspaper article about this and the effect it will have on the polar bear population. Remember, newspaper reports contain:

Headline

Important information

Less important information

Tail

Who?
When?
Where?
What?

Why?
How?

Conclusion

1. Acronyms are made up from the first letters of the names of organizations or things, (e.g., GPO – General Post Office).

   Below are acronyms from the passage on 'Sea Turtles'. Write their meanings.

   (a) ESA - _____   (b) USFWS - _____

   _____   _____

   _____   _____

2. Make an acronym for these titles.

   (a) Environmental Protection Agency _____

   (b) National Marine Fisheries Service _____

3. Place the six species of sea turtles into the correct boxes as ruled by the ESA of 1973.

Sea Turtles	
Threatened Species	Endangered Species

4. Why must a female sea turtle return to land? _____

5. What is so unusual about the nesting habits of sea turtles? _____

   _____

6. Record information about the largest and smallest sea turtles below.

Largest	Weight (kg)		Smallest	Weight (kg)
	Shell Length (m)			Shell Length (m)

7. Write to the address found on this site to find more detailed information about your favorite sea turtle.

8. Use the passage information to compare the differences in sea turtles. Choose two of your own to complete the chart.

SEA TURTLES

Name	Description	Weight	Adult Shell Size	Major Causes of Decline
Green Sea Turtle (Chelonia mydas)				
Loggerhead Sea Turtle (Caretta caretta)				

9. What action can the NMFS take to protect sea turtles from trawler fisherman?

_____

_____

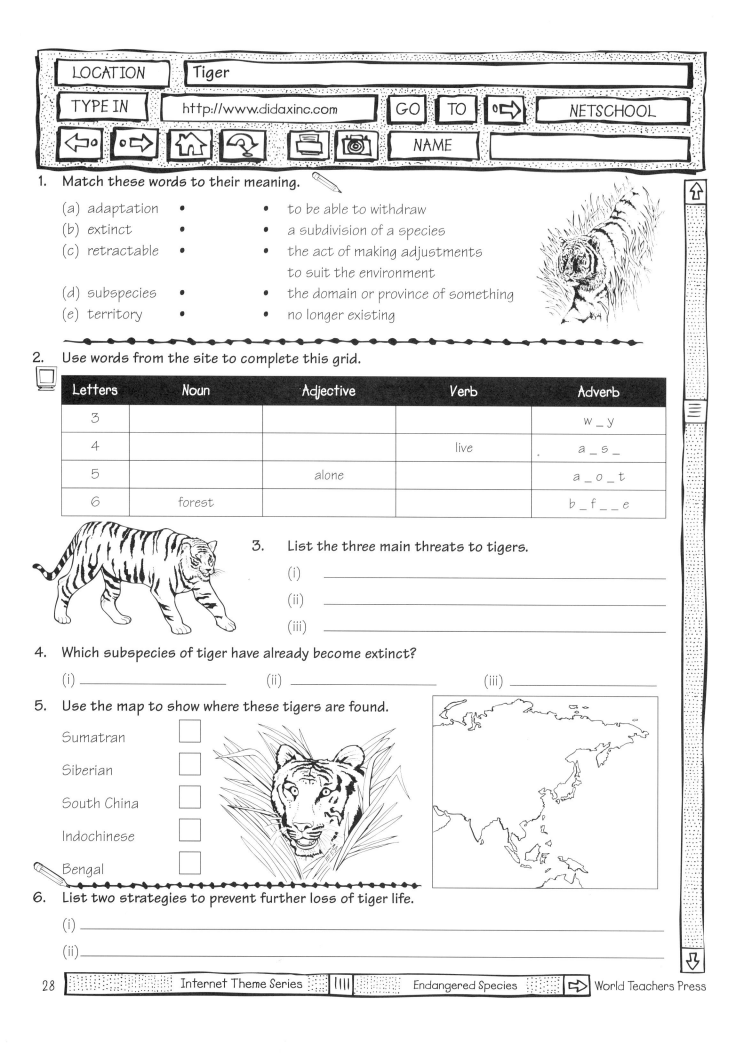

1. Match these words to their meaning.

   (a) adaptation •   • to be able to withdraw

   (b) extinct •   • a subdivision of a species

   (c) retractable •   • the act of making adjustments
                               to suit the environment

   (d) subspecies •   • the domain or province of something

   (e) territory •   • no longer existing

2. Use words from the site to complete this grid.

Letters	Noun	Adjective	Verb	Adverb
3				w _ y
4			live	a _ s _
5		alone		a _ o _ t
6	forest			b _ f _ _ e

3. List the three main threats to tigers.

   (i) _____

   (ii) _____

   (iii) _____

4. Which subspecies of tiger have already become extinct?

   (i) _____   (ii) _____   (iii) _____

5. Use the map to show where these tigers are found.

   Sumatran ☐

   Siberian ☐

   South China ☐

   Indochinese ☐

   Bengal ☐

6. List two strategies to prevent further loss of tiger life.

   (i) _____

   (ii) _____

NAME

7. The only way to save tigers may be by breeding them in captivity. Answer each of the following questions according to your beliefs.

(a) How much space does a zoo tiger need?

☐ Give the tiger as much space as possible, to recreate its natural environment.

☐ Limit the amount of space, so visitors can always see the tiger.

(b) Most zoo designers believe exhibits should imitate the animal's natural environment. Why?

☐ To make the animal feel at home.

☐ To educate people about the animal's natural habitat.

(c) How would you feed and care for a zoo tiger?

☐ Recreate, as much as possible, the tiger's natural feeding habits and diet.

☐ Develop a scientifically regulated diet and feeding schedule.

Can you use this information to design a safe, healthy zoo exhibit for a tiger?
Make sure you consider habitat, care and space. Display your exhibit in your classroom.

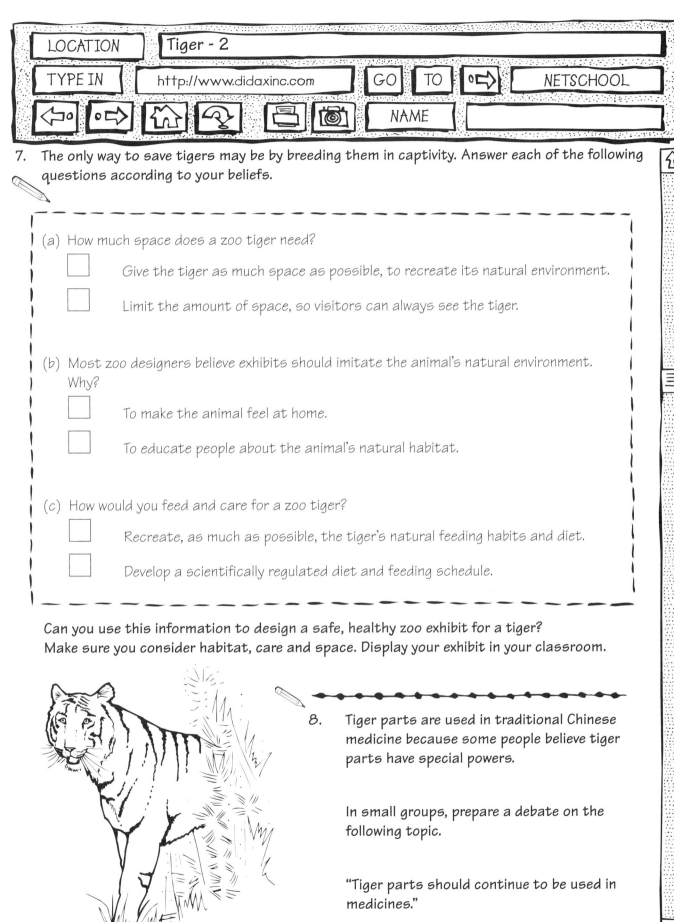

8. Tiger parts are used in traditional Chinese medicine because some people believe tiger parts have special powers.

In small groups, prepare a debate on the following topic.

"Tiger parts should continue to be used in medicines."

African Bush Elephant
Page 6
1. (a) bull   (b) cow   (c) calf
2. to protect themselves from sunburn and insect bites
3. roars, trumpets, rumbles, squeaks or chirps
4. matriarch
5. **Bull**
   Height - 10 - 12ft **Metric** - 3 - 3.6 m
   Weight - 10,000 - 12,000 lbs
   Metric - 4,500 - 5,400 kg
   Cow
   Height - 9 - 10ft **Metric** - 2.7 - 3 m
   Weight - 8,000 - 10,000 lbs
   Metric - 3,600 - 4,500 kg
6. elephant - herd
   wolves - pack
   lions - pride
   whales - pod
   seagulls - flock
7. **savanna** - a plain, characterised by coarse grasses and scattered tree growth
   imperative - not to be avoided or evaded
   vegetation - the plant life of a particular region
   nutrition - food; nutriment
8. Answers may vary
Page 7
9. Teacher check
10. **Elephant's Ears**
    (a) large ear flap can act as a receiver for animal calls from far away
    (b) to dispel heat from the brain and the rest of the body
    Elephant's Trunk
    (a) can pick up very small or large, heavy objects
    (b) can reach plants that no other herbivores can reach (besides giraffe)
    (c) to drink and spray water to cool
11. Teacher check

Raptor Facts
Page 8
1. water, weigh, white, wing, wingspan, winter
2. (a) **Nouns** = bald eagles, edge, rivers, lakes, seashores
   Verbs = nest
   (b) **Nouns** = bald eagles, fish
   Verbs = feed, catch

(c) **Nouns** = prey, waterfowl, birds, turtles, rabbits
   Verbs = feed, including
3. Teacher check   4. (c) 5. (a)
6. sheer size of the bird and its young
7. close to food source
Page 9
8. Teacher check   9. Teacher check

Bilby
Page 10
1. (a) alone - solitary
   (b) to move quickly - rapidly
   (c) no longer exists - extinct
   (d) escape
   (e) no hair - hairless
2. largest, Australia, soft, blue-gray, pointed, compact, Bilbies, large, silky, tails
3. (i) competition with introduced animals
   (ii) habitat changes/increased farming areas
4. studying habits, identifying distribution problems, managing habits, breeding in captivity
5. keeping cool, hearing predators
6. shelter, if threatened
Page 11
7. Teacher check   8. Teacher check
9. ninu, walpajirra
10. Answers may vary

Black Rhinoceros
Page 12
1. (a) dirt (b) grazer (c) frequently
   (d) changes (e) transient
2.

1 Syllable	2 Syllables	3 Syllables	4 Syllables
gray	species	national	rhinoceros
horns	desert	illegal	
threat	forest	habitat	
	demand	medicines	

3. (a) True   (b) False   (c) False
4. herbivore; grazes on grasses and twigs
5. (b)
6. Answers may vary
Page 13
7. Teacher check
8. two horns made of fibrous keratin

Cetaceans
Page 14
1. whales, dolphins, porpoises
2. sea mammals, breathe air, warm-blooded, bear live young, calves nursed by mothers
3. baleen and oil
4. collisions with vessels, oil spills, water pollution, entangled in fishing nets, human interference
5. cetaceans, development, impacts, inhabit, pollution, problem
6. Answers may vary
7. Answers may vary
Page 15
8. Teacher check 9. Teacher check

Cheetah
Page 16
1. Answers may vary
2. (i) hunted for furs
   (ii) vulnerable habitat destruction
   (iii) loss of natural prey
3. stalks prey and suffocates with a bite to the underside of the throat
4. avoids competition
5. coarse, short, tawny coat with small dark spots, paler underneath
6. Answers may vary
Page 17
7. Teacher check
8. Answers may vary
9. Teacher check

Dugong
Page 18
1. seagrass, underwater, sometimes, however, saltwater, into, farmland
2. **their** - there, they're
   hairs - hares
   sea - see   **where** - wear
   weigh - way   **tail** - tale
3. sea cows, graze on seagrasses
4.

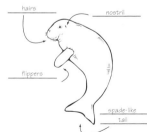

hairs   nostril

flippers

spade-like
tail

5. Answers may vary

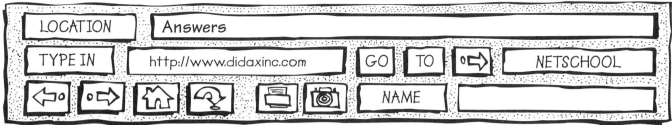
Page 19

6.

Shark Bay
Western Australia (WA)
Northern Territory (NT)
South Australia (SA)
Queensland (QLD)
New South Wales NSW
Victoria
Australian Capital Territory (ACT)
Tasmania (TAS)

7. Teacher check
8. Teacher check

Giant Panda
Page 20

1. only in south-west China
2. Summers - cool, monsoon rains
   Winter - snow and hail
3. (a) False (b) True (c) False
   (d) True (e) True (f) False
4. thick, woolly white coat with black
   eye patches, ears, shoulders, limbs
   and sometimes tip of tail, color
   acts as signal to other pandas
5. 99%   6. 12 hours
7. enlarged wristbone can be flexed like a
   thumb
8. Answers may vary

Page 21

9. Teacher check
10. (i) reduction of human activity
    (ii) management of bamboo
    (iii) extend panda reserves
11. Teacher check

Gorilla
Page 22

1. (a) to have many mountains
   (b) deserted
   (c) land which is low in comparison
       with surrounding areas
   (d) to have improved land by planting
       crops
   (e) the height above sea level
2. (a) always (b) small (c) often
   (d) taller   (e) lost
3. (a) False   (b) True
   (c) False   (d) True
4. generally remains on the ground
5. the way an animal or object moves
6. Answers may vary

Page 23

7. Teacher check 8. Teacher check

Polar Bear
Page 24

1. horse, stallion, mare
   sheep, ram, *ewe*
   swan, cob, pen
   rabbit, buck, doe
   chicken, rooster, *hen*
   deer, stag, hind
2. grass, drift, berry, field, flake, ball, man,
   cat, drop
3.

Height	Male	2.5 - 3 m	Female	2 - 2.5 m
Weight	Male	350 - 650 kg	Female	130 - 250 kg
Color	Fur	white to yellow	Skin	black
Eyes	dark brown, closely set			
Ears	small, rounded - lay flat when under water			
Tail	small - 7 to 12 cm long			
Coat	2.5 - 5 cm thick, dense, woolly, insulating layer of underhair			

4. (b)

Page 25

5. Teacher check   6. Teacher check
7. Teacher check

Sea Turtle
Page 26

1. (a) Endangered Species Act of 1973
   (b) US Fish and Wildlife Service
2. (a) EPA   (b) NMFS
3. **Threatened Species** - loggerhead, green
   ridley, olive ridley
   Endangered Species - Hawksbill, Kemp's
   ridley, leatherback
4. to lay eggs
5. nesting females return to the same
   beach on which they were born
6. **Largest**
   leatherback sea turtle
   Weight - 637 kg **Shell Length** - 1.85 m
   Smallest
   Kemp's ridley sea turtle
   Weight - 36 - 45 kg **Shell Length** 0.8 m
7. Teacher check

Page 27

8. Teacher check
9. requiring trawler fishermen to use Turtle
   Excluder Devices while fishing

Tiger
Page 28

1. (a) adaptation - the act of making
       adjustments to suit the
       environment

(b) extinct - no longer existing
(c) retractable - to be able to
    withdraw
(d) subspecies - a subdivision of
    a species
(e) territory - the domain or
    province of something
2. Answers may vary
3. (i) poaching (ii) habitat loss
   (iii) population fragmentation
4. (i) Bali (ii) Javan (iii) Caspian
5. Teacher check
6. Answers may vary

Page 29

7. Teacher check
8. Teacher check